OFF THE ROAD

PATRICK WRIGHT

David & Charles
Newton Abbot London

For John Braithwaite,
with thanks for the references and the dud battery.

British Library Cataloguing in Publication Data
Wright, Patrick
    Off the road.
    I. Title
    741.5'942   PN6737.W4/

    ISBN 0–7153–8818–5

Printed in Great Britain
by Redwood Burn Ltd, Trowbridge, Wilts.
for David & Charles Publishers plc
Brunel House Newton Abbot Devon

Foreword

By Lord Montagu of Beaulieu

Motoring humour started with the dawn of motoring and some of the cartoons provided a good social commentary as well as being funny. In the early days of motoring my father edited a weekly magazine called *Car Illustrated* and every week it contained many examples of such cartoons, one of the most distinguished contributors being Charles Sykes, the magazine's art editor but better known as the creator of the famous Rolls-Royce mascot.

As a child before the war, one of my favourite books was *The Punch Book of Motoring Humour* and subsequently, after I had founded the National Motor Museum at Beaulieu, I took an increasing interest in motoring humour and have several original cartoons hung in various rooms and offices.

Since the war I have very much admired the work of Russell Brockbank, David Langdon, Fougasse and other famous *Punch* contributors, but now I see that we have found a new motoring cartoonist in Patrick Wright, who certainly has brought motoring cartoons firmly into the 1980s. I am sure that in future years Patrick Wright's cartoons will be joining the other immortals on my walls.

Buying and selling.

DELICATE NEGOTIATIONS.

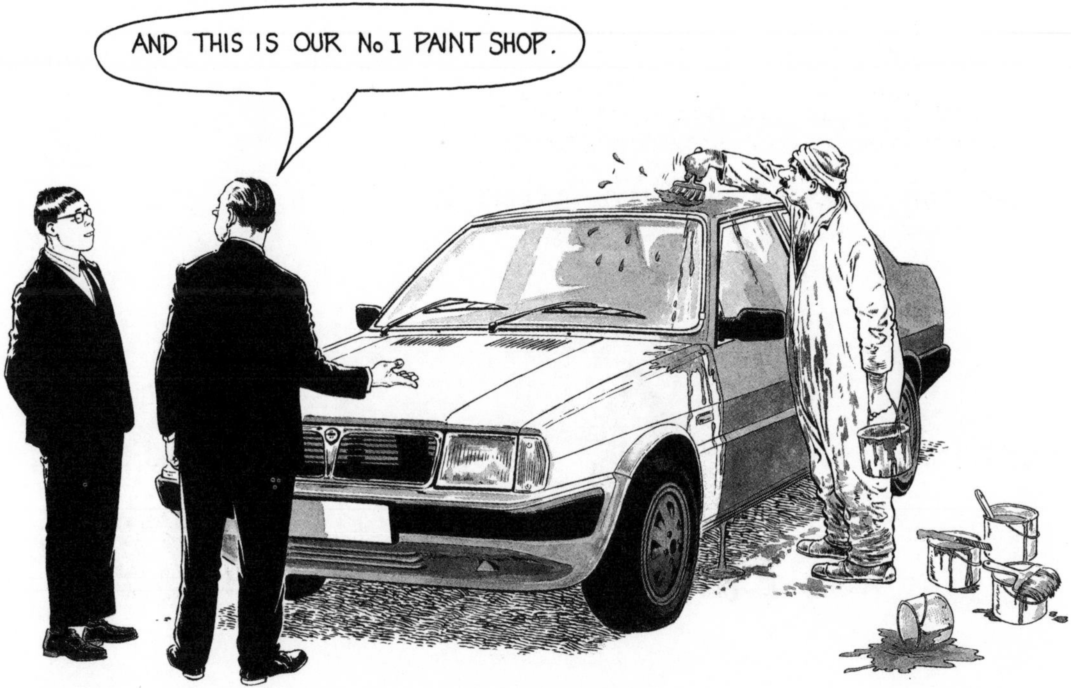
AND THIS IS OUR No I PAINT SHOP.

Accessories.

Routine maintenance.

Ferraris and other tart carts.

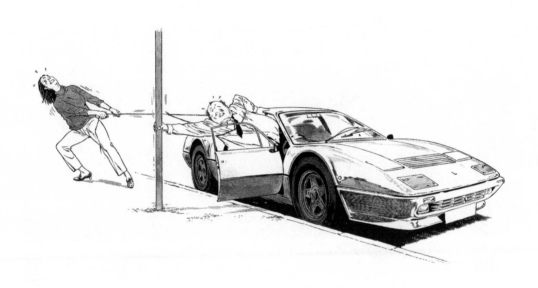

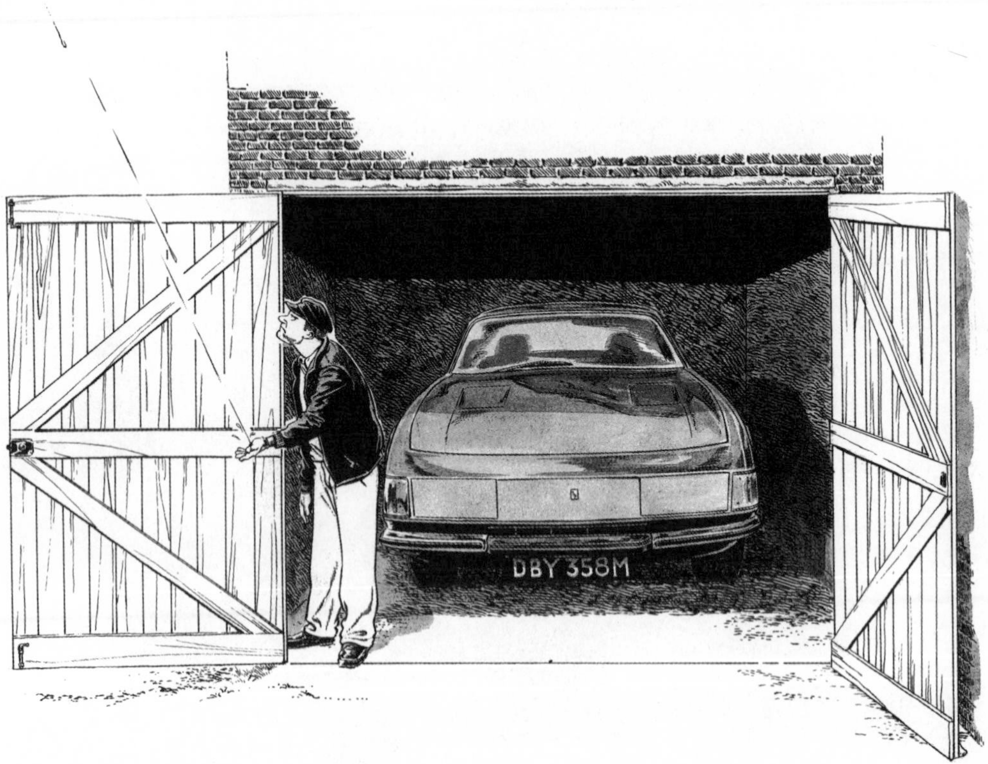
DBY 358M

On The Road.

Off the road.